Spanish Is Fun

Cuaderno de ejercicios

Book A

Heywood Wald
Former Assistant Principal
Foreign Language Department
Martin Van Buren High School
New York City

Lori Langer de Ramirez, Ed.D.
http://www.miscositas.com

AMSCO SCHOOL PUBLICATIONS, INC.,
a division of Perfection Learning®

Cover design by Delgado and Company Inc.
Text design by Progressive Information Technologies
Typeset by Lapiz Digital Services

Please visit our websites at:
www.amscopub.com and *www.perfectionlearning.com*

When ordering this book, please specify:
Softcover: ISBN 978-1-5311-0634-8 or **30928**
eBook: ISBN 978-1-5311-0637-9 or **30928D**

1 2 3 4 5 6 7 8 9   EBM   23 22 21 20 19 18 17

Printed in the United States of America

Preface

This *Cuaderno de ejercicios* supplements the practice materials in SPANISH IS FUN, BOOK A. The vocabulary and structural elements are closely coordinated with parallel chapters in the textbook.

While some exercises use techniques similar to those in the basal text, others extend the range of the materials. The workbook format provides opportunity for writing practice and intensive homework. The fourth edition of *Cuaderno de ejercicios* provides a more varied range of exercises and uses numerous illustrations to facilitate comprehension. More open-ended, personalized exercises were added to make this an even more enjoyable text for students and teachers.

Contents

EJERCICIO A

1

When you walk down the street, you see lots of people and things. Can you name in Spanish 20 objects or persons that are in the picture on the previous page?

1. el hotel   11. _____

2. _____   12. _____

3. _____   13. _____

4. _____   14. _____

5. _____   15. _____

6. _____   16. _____

7. _____   17. _____

8. _____   18. _____

9. _____   19. _____

10. _____   20. _____

EJERCICIO B

Match each noun to an adjective that describes it the best, and write your own sentences.

EXAMPLE: aeropuerto   grande
        El aeropuerto es grande

1. el sándwich   a. inteligente
2. el amigo   b. moderna
3. la fiesta   c. difícil
4. el auto   d. famosa
5. la lección   e. rápido
6. la actriz   f. interesante
7. la gorra   g. popular
8. el libro   h. delicioso
9. el perro   i. magnífico
10. el artista   j. adorable

1. _____

2. _____

3. _____

4. _____

5. _____

6. _____

7. _____

8. _____

9. _____

10. _____

EJERCICIO C

Answer these personal survey questions by checking off all adjectives that apply. Then write a sentence to state your answer.

EXAMPLE: ¿Cómo es tu madre?   ☐ grande   ☑ inteligente   ☑ sociable
Mi madre es inteligente y sociable.

1. ¿Cómo es tu padre?   ☐ popular   ☐ importante ☐ inteligente

   _____

2. ¿Cómo es tu computadora?   ☐ grande   ☐ rápida   ☐ moderna

   _____

3. ¿Cómo es tu mascota (perro o gato)? ☐ excelente ☐ adorable   ☐ grande

   _____

4. ¿Cómo es el jardín de tu casa?   ☐ grande   ☐ tropical   ☐ natural

   _____

5. ¿Cómo es tu mejor amigo/a? ☐ sociable ☐ inteligente ☐ popular

6. ¿Cómo es tu escuela? ☐ excelente ☐ grande ☐ importante

7. ¿Cómo es la bicicleta? ☐ importante ☐ grande ☐ moderna

8. ¿Cómo es tu estéreo? ☐ fácil ☐ excelente ☐ importante

9. ¿Cómo es tu casa? ☐ excelente ☐ importante ☐ grande

10. ¿Cómo es tu libro favorito? ☐ popular ☐ difícil ☐ importante

EJERCICIO D

Crucigrama. Fill in the correct Spanish words.

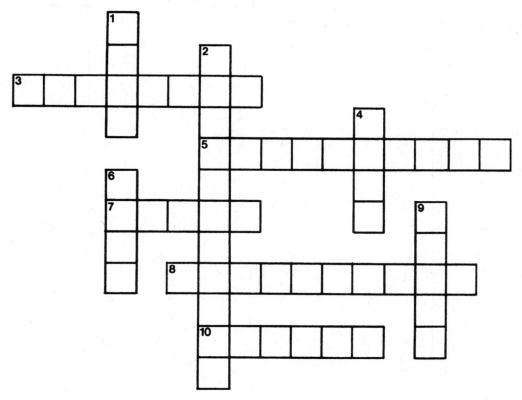

HORIZONTAL	VERTICAL
3. gasoline	1. flower
5. student	2. intelligent
7. radio	4. movies
8. secretary	6. train
10. theater	9. friend

EJERCICIO E

Buscapalabras. There are 14 Spanish nouns from this chapter hidden in the
puzzle. Circle them and list them below. The words may be read from left to right,
right to left, horizontally, or diagonally.

M	Ú	S	I	C	A	T	A
O	C	N	A	B	V	N	P
T	A	C	A	M	I	G	O
O	N	A	M	C	Ó	C	S
R	A	D	I	O	N	I	G
E	R	D	A	P	U	N	A
T	E	A	T	R	O	E	T
M	O	S	Q	U	I	T	O

1. _____   8. _____

2. _____   9. _____

3. _____   10. _____

4. _____   11. _____

5. _____   12. _____

6. _____   13. _____

7. _____   14. _____

EJERCICIO A

Make the following sentences plural. Be sure to change the noun, the adjective, and the verb.

EXAMPLE: El perro es grande.
             Los perros son grandes.

1. El disco compacto es popular.

   _____

2. El diccionario es importante.

   _____

3. La abuela es simpática.

   _____

4. El garaje es excelente.

   _____

5. La familia es moderna.

   _____

6. El hijo es sociable.

   _____

7. La plaza es ordinaria.

   _____

8. El tigre es cruel.

_____

9. La flor es natural.

_____

10. La banana es tropical.

_____

EJERCICIO B

Change the following sentences to the singular, making all necessary changes.

1. Los padres son sinceros.

_____

2. Los aviones son rápidos.

_____

3. Los médicos son excelentes.

_____

4. Las mujeres son norteamericanas.

_____

5. Las lámparas son magníficas.

_____

6. Los actores son populares.

_____

7. Los teléfonos son necesarios.

   _____

8. Los muchachos son terribles.

   _____

9. Las fiestas son románticas.

   _____

10. Los accidentes son horribles.

   _____

EJERCICIO C

Go to Actividad D on page 29 of the student's book. Write the plural of each word that is written in the singular and the singular for each word that is written in the plural.

1. _____   7. _____   13. _____

2. _____   8. _____   14. _____

3. _____   9. _____   15. _____

4. _____   10. _____   16. _____

5. _____   11. _____   17. _____

6. _____   12. _____   18. _____

EXAMPLE: la hamburguesa
          las hamburguesas

EJERCICIO D

Supply the matching noun. Use the correct article.

MASCULINO	FEMENINO
1. _____	la madre
2. el abuelo	_____
3. _____	la tía
4. el hijo	_____
5. _____	la hermana
6. el primo	_____

EJERCICIO E

Match the expressions in the left column with an appropriate expression in the right column. Write the matching letter in the space provided.

1. Buenos días, señorita.   _____
2. ¿Cómo te llamas?   _____
3. ¿Cómo estás?   _____
4. Hasta la vista, María.   _____
5. Mi perro se llama Duque.   _____
6. ¿Cómo se llaman las muchachas?   _____

a. Mi gato se llama Tigre.
b. Hasta luego, Pablo.
c. Muy bien, gracias.
d. Buenos días, señor profesor.
e. Se llaman Lola y Margarita.
f. Me llamo Paco.
g. Regular.
h. Antonio es el abuelo.

EJERCICIO F

Using the family tree, complete these sentences.

1. Andrés es el _____ de doña Francisca.

2. Don Antonio es el _____ de Andrés.

3. Andrés es el _____ de Eva.

4. Doña Josefa es la _____ de don Luis.

5. Doña Francisca es la _____ de don Lorenzo.

6. Eva es la _____ de Andrés.

7. Doña Francisca es la _____ de Eva y Andrés.

8. Don Luis es el _____ de Eva y Andrés.

9. Don Luis es el _____ de don Antonio.

10. Doña Francisca es la _____ de doña Rosa.

EJERCICIO G

Acróstico. Fill in the blanks with the Spanish meanings of the words below.

1. family
2. grandfather
3. necessary
4. aunt
5. airplane
6. nice
7. TV set
8. important
9. movies
10. opinion

1. F __ __ __ __ __ __

2. A __ __ __ __ __

3. N __ __ __ __ __ __ __ __

4. T __ __

5. Á __ __ __ __

6. S __ __ __ __ __ __ __

7. T __ __ __ __ __ __ __

8. I __ __ __ __ __ __ __ __ __

9. C __ __ __

10. O __ __ __ __ __

EJERCICIO H

Crucigrama de la familia. Fill in the correct words pertaining to family.

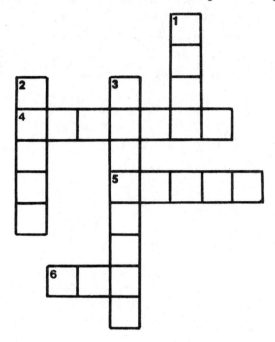

HORIZONTAL
4. grandparents
5. mother
6. uncle

VERTICAL
1. son
2. father
3. brothers (or brother and sister)

EJERCICIO I

The following 2 columns contain the same people expressed in a different way. Draw a line connecting these individuals.

A
1. el hijo de mi padre
2. el padre de mi madre
3. el hermano de mi madre
4. la hermana de mi madre
5. el hijo de mi tío

B
a) mi tío
b) mi tía
c) mi hermano
d) mi primo
e) mi abuelo

EJERCICIO A

Your little brother Juanito is very curious. As you walk down the street, he constantly asks: **¿Qué es esto** (this)? Identify what you see.

EXAMPLE: Juanito: —¿Qué es esto?
                            Usted: —Es una flor.

1. _____

2. _____

3. _____

4. _____

5. _____

6. _____

7. _____

8. _____

9. _____

10. _____

EJERCICIO B

Your Spanish teacher asks you to point out various classroom objects.

EXAMPLE:
Profesora: —¿Qué es esto?
Usted: —Es un cuaderno.

1. _____

2. _____

3. _____

4. _____

5. _____

6. _____

7. _____

8. _____

9. _____

10. _____

EJERCICIO C

Match the phrase in English to the phrase in Spanish.

1. the professor   **a.** el profesor   **b.** un profesor
2. a flower   **a.** la flor   **b.** una flor
3. an animal   **a.** el animal   **b.** un animal
4. a newspaper   **a.** el periódico   **b.** un periódico

 5. the mosquito   **a.** el mosquito   **b.** un mosquito

 6. the door   **a.** la puerta   **b.** una puerta

 7. a hat   **a.** el sombrero   **b.** un sombrero

 8. a garden   **a.** el jardín   **b.** un jardín

 9. a lesson   **a.** la lección   **b.** una lección

10. the paper   **a.** el papel   **b.** un papel

EJERCICIO D

Change the indefinite article to the definite article.

EXAMPLE: una silla   **la silla**

1. una flor _____

2. un periódico _____

3. una mujer _____

4. un animal _____

5. una fruta _____

6. un mosquito _____

7. un jardín _____

8. una clase _____

9. una lección _____

10. un primo _____

EJERCICIO E

Buscapalabras. In the puzzle, there are sixteen Spanish words. Circle them and list them below.

A	L	U	M	N	O	V	P	E
V	E	M	T	Í	A	E	I	S
I	C	A	T	Í	O	N	Z	C
Ó	H	P	U	E	R	T	A	U
N	E	A	T	I	Z	A	R	E
F	L	O	R	E	S	N	R	L
N	O	L	E	U	B	A	A	A
D	Í	A	N	Í	D	R	A	J

1. _____   9. _____

2. _____   10. _____

3. _____   11. _____

4. _____   12. _____

5. _____   13. _____

6. _____   14. _____

7. _____   15. _____

8. _____   16. _____

EJERCICIO F

Identify the people and objects in the picture.

EXAMPLE: Hay un escritorio.

1. _____

2. _____

3. _____

4. _____

5. _____

6. _____

7. _____

8. _____

9. _____

10. _____

11. _____

12. _____

EJERCICIO G

Name what's in Francisco's school locker. Make two lists: A) school items and B) personal items.

A	B
1. _____	1. _____
2. _____	2. _____
3. _____	3. _____
4. _____	4. _____
5. _____	5. _____
6. _____	6. _____
7. _____	7. _____

EJERCICIO A

Match each of the following statements with a picture, writing the corresponding number next to the picture that represents it.

1. Los amigos miran la televisión.

2. Enrique y Guillermo practican la música.

3. María visita a su mamá en el hospital.

4. Gloria compra un CD.

5. Nilda y Marta buscan una lente de contacto.

6. La mamá camina por el parque.

7. Los muchachos trabajan en casa.

8. Federico habla a la clase.

9. El papá llega a casa.

10. Los estudiantes entran en la escuela.

EJERCICIO B

Write full sentences about your own activities using your answers to Actividad A, page 53 of the student's book.

EXAMPLE: Miro la television por la tarde.

1.	mirar	_____	en un supermercado
2.	comprar	_____	un disco compacto
3.	escuchar	_____	la lección
4.	practicar	_____	un automóvil
5.	visitar	_____	el tren
6.	estudiar	_____	una gorra
7.	desear	_____	el piano
8.	tomar	_____	un museo
9.	hablar	_____	la televisión
10.	trabajar	_____	español

EJERCICIO C

Change the infinitive to agree with the subject.

EXAMPLE: yo/comprar un videojuego.
Yo compro un videojuego.

1. nosotros/mirar la televisión

   _____

2. mamá/trabajar en una librería

   _____

3. Uds./estudiar la lección

   _____

4. María/practicar piano

   _____

5. mis padres/llegar tarde

   _____

6. Ud./buscar el libro

   _____

7. tú/entrar en la clase

   _____

8. mi hermano/usar el automóvil

   _____

9. yo/preparar la comida

   _____

10. la profesora/hablar francés

    _____

EJERCICIO D

Change the subject and verb to the plural.

1. La señora compra la comida.

_____

2. Yo camino mucho.

_____

3. Tú llegas tarde.

_____

4. Él entra en la escuela.

_____

5. Ud. toma café.

_____

6. La secretaria busca el papel.

_____

7. Ella practica las frases.

_____

8. Mi padre trabaja mucho.

_____

9. Yo pregunto en la clase.

_____

10. El policía usa el teléfono.

_____

EJERCICIO E

Answer the questions according to the prompt in parentheses.

EXAMPLE:

¿Las señoras compran la comida? (la Señora Méndez ☑, la Señora García ☒)
→ **La Señora Méndez compra la comida, pero la Señora García no compra la comida.**

1. ¿Uds. llegan temprano? (yo ☑, Natalia ☒)

   _____

2. ¿Ellos preguntan mucho? (Javier ☑, Jaime ☒)

   _____

3. ¿Ustedes toman café? (mi amiga ☑, yo ☒)

   _____

4. ¿Uds. miran la televisión? (ellas ☑, tú y yo ☒)

   _____

5. ¿Uds. contestan bien? (yo ☑, mis amigos ☒)

   _____

6. ¿Los alumnos estudian mucho? (Juan Carlos ☑, Gisela ☒)

   _____

7. ¿Las muchachas bailan en la fiesta? (Margarita ☑, las hermanas Pérez ☒)

   _____

8. ¿Los muchachos compran un automóvil? (los primos ☑, Heriberto ☒)

   _____

9. ¿Ellos hablan francés? (mi madre ☑, mi padre ☒)

   _____

10. ¿Las estudiantes escuchan con atención? (Daniela ☑, Estafanía y yo ☒)

   _____

EJERCICIO F

Make the following sentences negative. Then write a sentence to make each statement affirmative.

EXAMPLE: La mujer trabaja en el hospital.
La mujer no trabaja en el hospital.
Ella trabaja en el banco.

1. Mi tía habla italiano.

   _____

   _____

2. Mis amigos toman el tren.

   _____

   _____

3. Yo deseo trabajar en casa.

   _____

   _____

4. Uds. llegan tarde.

   _____

   _____

5. Mi hermana camina por la ciudad.

   _____

   _____

6. Dolores baila en la escuela.

   _____

   _____

7. Mi mamá canta en la radio.

   _____

   _____

8. Nosotros buscamos el papel.

   _____

   _____

9. Juanito y José son primos.

   _____

   _____

10. Ud. estudia en casa.

   _____

   _____

EJERCICIO G

Change the following sentences to questions.

1. Tú trabajas en casa.

   _____

2. Ella camina por el parque.

   _____

3. Ellos compran chocolate.

   _____

4. La profesora habla rápidamente.

   _____

5. Uds. preparan la comida.

_____

6. Ud. toma la medicina.

_____

7. María escucha con atención.

_____

8. Uds. son norteamericanos.

_____

9. Ricardo mira por la ventana.

_____

10. Julio y Luis entran por la puerta.

_____

EJERCICIO H

Scrambled sentences. Each set of boxes contains a scrambled sentence. Rearrange the boxes in each set so that the words make a complete sentence.

1.

USAN	LOS HOMBRES Y LAS MUJERES	UNIDOS
AUTOMÓVILES	ESTADOS	EN LOS

_____

_____

2.

PARA	AUTOMÓVILES	AL
USAN	TRABAJO	IR

_____

_____

3.

HOSPITAL	LOS MÉDICOS	AL
VAN	AUTOMÓVIL	EN

_____

_____

4.

LOS HOMBRES	LAS MUJERES	Y
DE COMPRAS	EN AUTOMÓVIL	VAN

_____

_____

5.

AUTOMÓVILES	GASOLINA	GRANDES
MUCHA	USAN	LOS

_____

_____

6.

LA	UN	ES
SOLUCIÓN	PEQUEÑO	AUTOMÓVIL

_____

_____

EJERCICIO A

What's in the park?

En el parque hay...

1. _____ muchachos.

2. _____ muchachas.

3. _____ perros.

4. _____ gatos.

5. _____ bicicletas.

6. _____ estéreo.

7. _____ bebés.

8. _____ flores.

EJERCICIO B

Look at these images and write a sentence to represent how many of each item you or your teacher will need for the first day of classes.

EXAMPLE: yo + 3 +   **Yo necesito tres cuadernos.**

1. La profesora + 15 +   _____

2. Yo + 8 +

_____

3. La profesora + 6 +

_____

4. La profesora + 9 +

_____

5. Yo + 23 +

_____

6. La profesora + 2 + _____

7. Yo + 30 + _____

8. Yo + 4 + _____

9. Yo + 1 + _____

10. La profesora + 14 + _____

EJERCICIO C

Write the numbers in the series.

1. uno, dos, tres, _____, _____, _____

2. dos, cuatro, seis, _____, _____, _____

3. uno, tres, cinco, _____, _____, _____

4. cinco, diez, _____, _____, _____

5. uno, dos, cuatro, _____, _____, _____

6. diez, nueve, ocho, _____, _____, _____

EJERCICIO D

An escaped prisoner is attempting to flee the country and cross the border into Mexico. A Mexican official is broadcasting the license plate number of one stolen car of special interest: SEIS, UNO, CINCO, DOS, SEIS, SEIS. Read the following license plates and then circle the number the authorities are looking for.

1. **9940 952**

2. **482 519**

3. **5320 157**

4. **653 2211**

5. **397 973**

6. **828 472**

7. **236 891**

8. **615 266**

EJERCICIO E

Here are some phone numbers. Say them and then write them out in Spanish.

EXAMPLE: (718) 209 1854
siete uno ocho dos cero nueve uno ocho cinco cuatro

1. (718) 208 3874

_____

2. (212) 113 5687

_____

3. (805) 342 6701

_____

4. (516) 998 3214

_____

5. (307) 763 8520

_____

6. (801) 576 1113

_____

7. (890) 890 2222

_____

8. (201) 434 1010

_____

9. (817) 325 6690

_____

10. (609) 220 8314

_____

EJERCICIO F

How good are you in arithmetic? Write out these operations in Spanish supplying the correct answer.

EXAMPLE: $7 - 2 =$ **Siete menos dos son cinco.**

1. $9 - 5 =$ _____

2. $8 + 1 =$ _____

3. $15 \div 5 =$ _____

4. $4 \times 3 =$ _____

5. $30 - 20 =$ _____

6. $16 + 2 =$ _____

7. $30 \div 3 =$ _____

8. $14 \times 2 =$ _____

9. $19 - 1 =$ _____

10. $11 + 0 =$ _____

EJERCICIO G

You just made some new friends during our semester abroad in Valencia, Spain. Write down your friends phone numbers and say them aloud to verify that they are correct.

EXAMPLE: 22-59-03
         veintidós, diecinueve, cero tres

1. _____

2. _____

3. _____

4. _____

5. _____

EJERCICIO H

Los Gigantes have just finished playing **Los Atléticos**. Write out the score in Spanish, inning by inning, and then figure out the final score.

Entrada	1	2	3	4	5	6	7	8	9	**Anotación final**
Gigantes	0	0	1	2	1	0	0	0	5	
Atléticos	1	3	0	0	1	2	0	0	1	

           LOS GIGANTES   LOS ATLÉTICOS

1. _____ cero _____ uno _____

2. _____

3. _____

4. _____

5. _____

6. _____

7. _____

8. _____

9. _____

Anotación final _____

EJERCICIO I

¿Sí o no? Mr. Molina is correcting the math papers of his fourth-grade students. If a result is wrong, fill in the correct answer.

1. Cuatro y tres son **siete.** _____

2. Cinco por cinco son **veinte.** _____

3. Nueve menos dos son **seis.** _____

4. Ocho dividido por cuatro son **dos.** _____

5. Once y doce son **veintitrés.** _____

6. Quince menos cinco son **diez.** _____

7. Tres por dos son **seis.** _____

8. Diez dividido por diez es **cero.** _____

9. Quince y catorce son **treinta.** _____

10. Diecisiete menos dieciséis es **uno.** _____

EJERCICIO J

Write the numbers that come before and after the following numbers.

1. _____ dos _____

2. _____ cinco _____

3. _____ ocho _____

4. _____ diez _____

5. _____ doce _____

6. _____ quince _____

7. _____ diecisiete _____

8. _____ veinte _____

9. _____ veintitrés _____

10. _____ veintinueve _____

EJERCICIO K

Rubén is very well organized. He writes down all the important dates on his calendar. When do the following events occur?

MAYO 2020						
LUNES	MARTES	MIÉRCOLES	JUEVES	VIERNES	SÁBADO	DOMINGO
		1 Examen de español	2	3	4 Función de teatro	5
6 Lección de música	7 Concierto de rock	8	9 Médico	10	11	12 Día de las madres
13	14	15	16	17	18 Fiesta en casa de Pepe	19
20	21	22 Cumpleaños de María	23	24 Dentista	25	26
27	28 Visita a los abuelos	29 Examen de inglés	30	31		

EXAMPLE: **¿Cuándo es el Día de las Madres?**
Es el día doce.

1. ¿Cuándo es la visita al médico?

   _____

2. ¿Cuándo es el concierto de rock?

   _____

3. ¿Cuándo es el examen de español?

   _____

4. ¿Cuándo es la fiesta en casa de Pepe?

   _____

5. ¿Cuándo es la visita al dentista?

_____

6. ¿Cuándo es la lección de música?

_____

7. ¿Cuándo es la visita a los abuelos?

_____

8. ¿Cuándo es el examen de inglés?

_____

9. ¿Cuándo es el cumpleaños (*birthday*) de María?

_____

10. ¿Cuándo es la función (*show*) de teatro?

_____

EJERCICIO A

All the clocks in this store have to be set. They all have different times. Can you tell the time on each one?

1. _____

2. _____

3. _____

4. _____

5. _____

6. _____

7. _____

8. _____

9. _____

10. _____

EJERCICIO B

Un día en la vida de Elena. Describe Elena's busy day. Tell what she does and at what time.

1.   8:30

2.   9:00

3.

4.   10:00

5. 10:45

6. 11:30

7. 3:30

8. 4:00

9. 6:50

10. 8:00

1. A las ocho y media Elena camina a la escuela.

2. _____

3. _____

4. _____

5. _____

6. _____

7. _____

8. _____

9. _____

10. _____

EJERCICIO C

¿A qué hora llega el tren? Tell at what time the train arrives according to the following schedule.

EXAMPLE: Madrid: 11:15 A.M.
   El tren llega a Madrid a las once y cuarto de la mañana.

1. Barcelona: 7:35 A.M.

   _____

2. Málaga: 8:20 A.M.

   _____

3. Zaragoza: 12:15 A.M.

   _____

4. Bilbao: 4:39 P.M.

   _____

5. Granada: 5:50 A.M.

   _____

6. Cádiz 1:17 P.M.

   _____

7. Burgos: 6:12 A.M.

   _____

8. Salamanca: 12:00 midnight

   _____

9. Segovia: 2:30 P.M.

_____

10. Toledo: 10:45 P.M.

_____

EJERCICIO D

Answer the following questions according to the time that each clock shows.

1. ¿A qué hora desayunas?

_____

2. ¿A qué hora llegas a la escuela?

_____

3. ¿A qué hora es tu clase de español?

_____

4. ¿A qué hora es tu clase de inglés?

_____

5. ¿A qué hora terminan las clases?

_____

6. ¿A qué hora regresas a casa?

_____

7. ¿A qué hora miras la televisión?

_____

EJERCICIO E

Are you an early bird or a night owl? Take this survey to find out. Answer each question and then add up your points.

1. ¿Cuándo estudias las lecciones?
   a. a las siete de la mañana (1 punto)
   b. a las tres de la tarde (3 puntos)
   c. a las diez de la noche (5 puntos)

2. ¿Cuándo hablas por teléfono?
   a. a las ocho de la mañana (1 punto)
   b. a las cinco de la tarde (3 puntos)
   c. a las nueve de la noche (5 puntos)

3. ¿Cuándo preparas la tarea?
   a. a las seis de la mañana (1 punto)
   b. a las cuatro de la tarde (3 puntos)
   c. a las once de la noche (5 puntos)

4. ¿Cuándo llegas a casa durante los fines de semana?
   a. a las siete de la noche (1 punto)
   b. a las nueve de la noche (3 puntos)
   c. a las doce de la mañana (5 puntos)

5. ¿Cuándo miras la televisión?
   a. a las nueve de la mañana (1 punto)
   b. a las cinco y media de la tarde (3 puntos)
   c. a las diez de la noche (5 puntos)

6. ¿Cuándo mandas correos electrónicos?
   a. a las seis y cuarto de la mañana (1 punto)
   b. a las dos de la tarde (3 puntos)
   c. a las once y media de la noche (5 puntos)

7. ¿Cuándo lees una revista?
   a. a las ocho de la mañana (1 punto)
   b. a la una de la tarde (3 puntos)
   c. a las once de la noche (5 puntos)

8. ¿Cuándo miras películas?
   a. a las nueve de la mañana (1 punto)
   b. a las cuatro de la tarde (3 puntos)
   c. a las diez de la noche (5 puntos)

9. ¿Cuándo escribes cartas a tu familia?
   a. a las diez de la mañana (1 punto)
   b. a las cinco de la tarde (3 puntos)
   c. a las nueve y media de la noche (5 puntos)

10. ¿Cuándo usas la computadora?
    a. a las cinco de la mañana (1 punto)
    b. a la una de la tarde (3 puntos)
    c. a las doce de la noche (5 puntos)

→ If you scored between 10 and 20 points, you are an early bird!
→ If you scored between 21 and 35 points, you are neither an early bird nor a night owl!
→ If you scored between 36 and 50 points, you are a night owl!

EJERCICIO F

El viaje en autobús (*The bus trip*)

> **¿A qué hora llega?** At what time does it arrive?
> **¿A qué hora sale?** At what time does it leave?

A tourist bus starting out from Cádiz travels through Spain. The arrival and departure times are given for each city. Write down when the bus arrives at and leaves from the cities indicated.

EXAMPLE: Málaga   8:10 **Llega a Málaga a las ocho y diez.**
8:30 **Sale de Málaga a las ocho y treinta.**

1. Granada   9:15 _____

           9:20 _____

2. Córdoba   10:20 _____

           10:35 _____

3. Valencia   12:00 _____

           12:30 _____

4. Toledo   1:45   _____

         2:00   _____

5. Madrid   2:50   _____

         3:05   _____

6. Segovia   3:55   _____

         4:10   _____

7. Burgos   5:05   _____

         5:20   _____

8. Bilbao   6:30   _____

EJERCICIO G

The following arrivals and departures are being announced over the loudspeaker. Repeat them aloud.

1. El vuelo de Aeroperú llega a la 1:00.

2. El vuelo de Mexicana llega a las 2:45.

3. El vuelo de Aerolíneas Argentinas llega a las 7:30.

4. El vuelo de Iberia llega a las 12:15.

5. El vuelo de Aero México llega a las 3:10.

6. El vuelo de Dominicana llega a las 8:50.

7. El vuelo de Ecuatoriana sale a las 10:00.

8. El vuelo de Avianca sale a las 9:25.

9. El vuelo de Viasa sale a las 4:35.

10. El vuelo de Varig sale a las 11:20.

EJERCICIO H

Write out in Spanish at what time you usually do the following activities.

EXAMPLE: comer el desayuno
Como el desayuno a las siete de la mañana.

1. caminar a la parada de autobús

   _____

2. tomar el autobús

   _____

3. entrar en la escuela

   _____

4. estudiar español en la biblioteca

   _____

5. comer el almuerzo

   _____

6. llegar a casa

   _____

7. usar la computadora

   _____

8. practicar deportes

   _____

9. preparar la tarea

   _____

10. mirar la televisión

    _____

EJERCICIO I

¡Estoy tarde! You're late for an appointment. Say the time on each of the digital clocks below. Then express when your appointment was scheduled for.

EXAMPLE: **Son las dos y cinco.**

¡Estoy tarde! Tengo una cita **a las dos**.

2:05	5:05	6:05
10:05	3:10	4:10
8:10	2:20	5:20
7:20	11:20	12:25

1. _____

2. _____

3. _____

4. _____

5. _____

6. _____

7. _____

8. _____

9. _____

10. _____

11. _____

12. _____

EJERCICIO A

Change the infinitive to agree with the subject.

1. nosotros/aprender español

_____

2. mamá/comer muchas frutas

_____

3. yo/ver el parque

_____

4. Ud./responder a la pregunta

_____

5. mis padres/beber agua fría

_____

6. Francisco/comprender la lección

_____

7. los muchachos/creer al profesor

_____

8. tú/vender la casa

_____

9. Uds./querer el periódico

   _____

10. yo/ver el tren

    _____

EJERCICIO B

Change the subject and verb to the corresponding plural or singular form as needed.

1. La alumna aprende mucho.

   _____

2. Nosotros sabemos la regla.

   _____

3. Tú corres por la calle.

   _____

4. Ellas beben soda.

   _____

5. Los muchachos beben café.

   _____

6. La secretaria comprende las instrucciones.

   _____

7. Ustedes venden las blusas.

   _____

8. Mi padre cree la historia.

   _____

9. Yo leo el periódico.

_____

10. Los hombres ven el edificio.

_____

EJERCICIO C

Create a question using the cues, then answer according to the cue in parenthesis. Follow the example.

EXAMPLE: ellos / platos (sí)
          ¿Venden platos? → Sí, venden platos.

1. Carlos / los videojuegos (sí)

_____

2. tú / televisores (no, radios)

_____

3. María y Ana / blusas (no, camisas)

_____

4. Rosa / bicicletas (sí)

_____

5. usted / vaqueros (no, pantalones cortos)

_____

6. Milagros / teléfonos (sí)

_____

7. José y Santiago / computadoras (sí)

   _____

8. nosotros / libros (no, cuadernos)

   _____

EJERCICIO D

¡Pobre Juan! He is always doing something wrong in school. Complete each statement with a verb in the singular and a word or phrase that makes sense.

1. Los alumnos aprenden la lección, pero Juan...

   _____

2. Los estudiantes llegan temprano a la escuela, pero Juan...

   _____

3. Las señoritas corren por la calle y Juan...

   _____

4. Uds. responden bien, pero Juan...

   _____

5. Nostras comprendemos el examen, pero Juan...

   _____

7. Los muchachos escuchan atentamente al profesor, pero Juan...

   _____

8. Uds. no hablan durante el examen, pero Juan...

   _____

9. Ellos leen el libro en la biblioteca, pero Juan...

_____

10. Las muchachas hacen la tarea, pero Juan...

_____

EJERCICIO E

Make the following sentences negative.

1. La mujer aprende francés.

_____

2. Mis amigos comen en la cafetería.

_____

3. Yo corro con mi perro.

_____

4. Uds. responden en inglés.

_____

5. Mi hermana bebe mucho café.

_____

6. Dolores comprende las palabras.

_____

7. Mi hermano cree la historia.

_____

8. Nosotros vendemos un escritorio.

_____

9. Juanito y José leen libros españoles.

_____

10. Ud. quiere un helado de chocolate.

_____

EJERCICIO F

Match the statements to the questions.

A

1. Yo aprendo español.
2. Ella come ensalada.
3. Ellos corren rápidamente.
4. La profesora responde a los estudiantes.
5. Uds. beben mucha leche.
6. Ella comprende la lección.
7. María cree la historia.
8. Uds. venden sándwiches.
9. Ricardo lee una novela.
10. Julio y Luis ven un perro en el parque.

B

a. ¿Qué come ella?
b. ¿Qué comprende ella?
c. ¿Qué cree María?
d. ¿Quienes corren rápidamente?
e. ¿Qué lee Ricardo?
f. ¿Qué venden Uds.?
g. ¿Qué ven en el parque?
h. ¿Qué beben Uds.?
i. ¿Quién responde a los estudiantes?
j. ¿Qué aprendes?

EJERCICIO G

Using an **-er** verb, tell what each person is doing.

                    María

1.

_____

Los muchachos

2.

El policía

3.

Antonio

4.

El bebé

5.

La niña

6.

La señorita

7.

Los estudiantes

$$3x + 30 = 45$$
$$x = ?$$

8.

Yo

$$x + 2y = 40$$

9.

El turista

10.

EJERCICIO H

Each set of boxes contains a scrambled sentence. Rearrange the boxes in each set so that the words make a complete sentence.

1.

PEPE	DOCE	DE
AÑOS	UN MUCHACHO	ES

2.

PERRO	LOBO	MUY
UN	INTELIGENTE	ES

3.

Y	MUY	COME
GRANDE	MUCHO	ES

4.

PARA	LA COMIDA	TRABAJA
DE LOBO	COMPRAR	PEPE

_____

_____

5.

TODOS	PEPE	LOS
DÍAS	PERIÓDICOS	VENDE

_____

_____

6.

TAREAS	Y PREPARA	LA
ESCUELA	LAS	PARA

_____

_____

EJERCICIO A

Write a suitable color for the following objects.

1. _____

2. _____

3. _____

4. _____

5. _____

6. _____

7. _____

8. _____

9. _____

EJERCICIO B

Write a complete sentence in which you give the color of the following.

EXAMPLE: **El televisor es negro.**

1. la casa _____

2. la carne _____

3. el árbol _____

4. la banana _____

5. la leche _____

6. el cielo _____

7. el océano _____

8. el teléfono _____

EJERCICIO C

You are watching a **telenovela** on TV, but your cable reception is not is good and some of the dialog keeps dropping out. Fill in the blanks in this conversation with the correct form of the adjective in parentheses.

MARTINA: ¡Ay, papá! Estoy _____. El examen es
                                       1. (nervioso)

               _____.
                2. (difícil)

PADRE: Sí, mi amor, pero es un examen _____.
                                     3. (necesario)

MARTINA: Es verdad. Y todos los alumnos son _____.
                                     4. (inteligente)

PADRE: Y tú eres la muchacha más inteligente. Y también la más

               _____.
                5. (bonito)

MARTINA: Gracias, Papá. ¿Dónde está tu amigo, el señor _____?

6. (norteamericano)

PADRE: Está en la oficina, en una reunión con el director de la compañía

_____.

7. (español)

MARTINA: ¿Es una reunión muy _____?

8. (importante)

PADRE: Sí. Hay un problema _____.

9. (serio)

MARTINA: Buena suerte, papá.

PADRE: Gracias. Hasta luego Martina.

EJERCICIO D

Emphasize the quality of something or someone by showing the opposite.

EXAMPLE: Mi hermana es bonita. **No es fea.**

1. Lola es inteligente.   No es _____.

2. El muchacho es alto.   No es _____.

3. Mis tíos son ricos.   No son _____.

4. María es rubia.   No es _____.

5. Mi padre es gordo.   No es _____.

6. El estudiante es inteligente.   No es _____.

7. Las palabras son fáciles.   No son _____.

8. Los libros son nuevos.   No son _____.

9. El gato es negro.   No es _____.

10. Las bicicletas son nuevas.   No son _____.

EJERCICIO E

Here are some opposites. Can you label them?

1. _____ _____   2. _____ _____

3. _____ _____   4. _____ _____

5. _____ _____   6. _____ _____

7. _____ _____   8. _____ _____

EJERCICIO F

Underline the adjective that correctly describes the subject.

1. Las avenidas son (grande, grandes).

2. Mis hermanas son (bonito, bonita, bonitos, bonitas).

3. El hombre es (rico, rica, ricos, ricas).

4. La lección es (difícil, difíciles).

5. El árbol es (verde, verdes).

6. Los gatos son animales (pequeño, pequeña, pequeños, pequeñas).

7. Los profesores de mi escuela son (inteligente, inteligentes).

8. La pizza y los espaguetis son comidas (italiano, italiana, italianos, italianas).

9. Tengo unas plumas (rojo, roja, rojos, rojas).

10. Las escuelas de mi ciudad son (moderno, moderna, modernos, modernas).

EJERCICIO G

Write four sentences describing the people and animals pictured below. Use the adjectives you have learned.

1.

2.

3.

_____
_____
_____
_____

4.

_____
_____
_____
_____

EJERCICIO H

Think about four famous people or characters. Write five or more words to describe each person.

Famous Person/Character	Name	Description
Movie star		
Singer		
TV person		
Cartoon character		

EJERCICIO A

It's career day and all the students are indicating what they want to be when they grow up. Write each person's dreams in Spanish.

1. Lupe quiere ser _____.

2. Paco y Geraldo quieren ser _____.

3. Javier quiere ser _____.

4. Maritza y Mariluz quieren ser _____.

5. Armando quiere ser _____.

6. El hermano de Raúl quiere ser _____.

7. Angel quiere ser _____.

8. Ana quiere ser _____.

9. Carmen quiere ser _____.

10. Miguel quiere ser _____.

EJERCICIO B

Using the correct form of the verb **ser**, tell where everyone is from.

EXAMPLE: Manuel/Puerto Rico
Manuel es de Puerto Rico.

1. María/la República Dominicana

_____

2. yo/España

_____

3. tú/Cuba

_____

4. él/Costa Rica

_____

5. ella/Venezuela

   _____

6. Ud./Colombia

   _____

7. nosotros/los Estados Unidos

   _____

8. Uds./Chile

   _____

9. ellos/Guatemala

   _____

10. Lola y Rosa/Honduras

   _____

EJERCICIO C

Complete with the proper form of **ser**.

1. Yo _____ norteamericano.

2. Luis y yo _____ los hijos del Sr. González.

3. Francisco y yo _____ hermanos.

4. ¿_____ ella tu prima?

5. Mi madre _____ francesa.

6. La familia no _____ grande.

7. ¿_____ ustedes abogados?

8. Tú _____ un alumno inteligente.

9. Pablo y yo _____ ricos.

10. Ellos _____ médicos.

EJERCICIO D

Answer the following questions either affirmatively or negatively.

EXAMPLE: ¿Es Ud. alto?
No, yo soy bajo.

1. ¿Es grande la escuela?

_____

2. ¿Son blancas las rosas?

_____

3. ¿Son inglesas tus amigas?

_____

4. ¿Es Ud. mexicano?

_____

5. ¿Es joven la abuela?

_____

6. ¿Es Ud. un alumno inteligente?

_____

7. ¿Son pequeños los elefantes?

_____

8. ¿Es azul su automóvil?

_____

9. ¿Son las flores feas?

_____

10. ¿Es difícil la lección?

_____

EJERCICIO E

Make the following sentences plural.

1. Él es cubano.

   _____

2. Yo soy profesor.

   _____

3. ¿Es Ud. dentista?

   _____

4. ¿No eres tú francés?

   _____

5. Ella es abogada.

   _____

6. Mi tía es italiana.

   _____

7. Mi hermana es secretaria.

   _____

8. El muchacho es el hijo de Pablo.

   _____

9. Tú eres inteligente.

   _____

10. Yo soy norteamericano.

    _____

EJERCICIO F

Make the following sentences singular.

1. Las familias son grandes.

   _____

2. Somos artistas.

   _____

3. ¿Qué son ustedes?

   _____

4. Ellas son españolas.

   _____

5. Las lecciones son fáciles.

   _____

6. Los papeles son blancos.

   _____

7. ¿Son Uds. argentinos?

   _____

8. Ellos son actores.

   _____

9. Uds. son muy inteligentes.

   _____

10. Nosotros somos enfermeros.

    _____

EJERCICIO A

Using the **-ir** verbs you have learned, tell what the following are doing.

1. El policía _____ la puerta.

2. El gato _____ del jardín.

3. Yo _____ de la escuela.

4. Mi mamá _____ las frutas.

5. El perro _____ en la casa.

6. La secretaria _____ en el papel.

7. La enfermera _____ al paciente. **8.** La abuela _____ la carta.

9. El bombero _____ al edificio. **10.** La profesora _____ la pintura.

EJERCICIO B

Answer each question according to the cue in parentheses.

Example: ¿Quién toca la puerta? (ella) → **Ella toca la puerta.**

1. ¿Quién abre la ventana? (ella) _____

2. ¿Quién sube la escalera? (el policía) _____

3. ¿Quién divide el pan? (yo) _____

4. ¿Quién cubre la cama? (Ud.) _____

5. ¿Quién escribe una carta? (mis padres) _____

6. ¿Quién describe la situación? (nosotros) _____

7. ¿Quién recibe el dinero? (tú) _____

8. ¿Quién vive en España? (el abogado) _____

9. ¿Quién sale de la casa? (ellas) _____

10. ¿Quién vive en Italia? (tú) _____

EJERCICIO C

Change the subject and verb to the plural.

1. La alumna abre la puerta.

   _____

2. Tú recibes el dinero.

   _____

3. Yo subo al árbol.

   _____

4. Él escribe una carta.

   _____

5. Ud. trae la sopa.

   _____

6. La secretaria vive lejos.

   _____

7. Ella sale de la escuela.

   _____

8. Mi padre pone la mesa.

   _____

9. Yo sé mucho.

   _____

10. El hombre da regalos a su familia.

EJERCICIO D

Martica and Yesenia always have difference of opinion. Finish Yesenia's statements using the right forms of the verbs.

Martica: Las tareas de las clases siempre son muy difíciles.
Yesenia: Pero la tarea de esta noche **no es muy difícil.**

1. Martica: Los alumnos traen los libros.
   Yesenia: Pero el alumno nuevo no _____.

2. Martica: Nosotros dividimos el trabajo en la clase de ciencias.
   Yesenia: Pero Héctor no _____.

3. Martica: Las profesoras suben al segundo piso.
   Yesenia: Pero la profesora de arte no _____.

4. Martica: Nuestras amigas viven en Buenos Aires.
   Yesenia: Pero Penélope no _____.

5. Martica: Las chicas de la clase saben mucho.
   Yesenia: Pero Isabel no _____.

6. Martica: Ellas ponen los libros en el escritorio.
   Yesenia: Pero yo no _____.

7. Martica: Los muchachos reciben buenas notas.
   Yesenia: Pero Heriberto no _____.

8. Martica: Ustedes describen bien la escuela.
   Yesenia: Pero Ud. no _____.

9. Martica: Los directores viven en un edificio cerca de la escuela.
   Yesenia: Pero el director principal no _____.

10. Martica: Las alumnas salen del tren.
    Yesenia: Pero Mariluz no _____.

EJERCICIO E

Complete the sentences.

1. (is leaving) El avión _____ ahora.

2. (receive) Mis hermanas _____ muchos regalos.

3. (doesn't cover) Ana _____ su cuaderno.

4. (describe) Ella no _____ su escuela.

5. (bring) Yo _____ la comida.

6. (live) Uds. _____ en California.

7. (know) Mis padres _____ de todo.

8. (give) Yo _____ el dinero al señor de la tienda.

9. (write) Nosotros _____ muchas cartas.

10. (open) Luis y Manuel _____ la ventana.

EJERCICIO F

Answer the following questions.

1. ¿Dónde vives?

   _____

2. ¿Cuándo escribes correos electrónicos?

   _____

3. ¿Cuándo recibes un regalo?

   _____

4. ¿Qué sabes hacer muy bien?

   _____

5. ¿Qué llevas a la escuela todos los días?

   _____

6. ¿Cuándo preparas la tarea de la escuela?

   _____

7. ¿A qué hora sales de la escuela?

   _____

8. ¿Cuál es el regalo de cumpleaños perfecto para tu mejor amigo/a?

   _____

9. ¿Quién divide el trabajo en la clase de ciencias?

   _____

10. ¿Qué deportes practicas?

    _____

EJERCICIO G

Write a question based on each statement. Then answer in the negative and write an alternate ending to the statement. Follow the example.

EXAMPLE: escribir una frase en la pizarra (el profesor)
  → **¿El profesor escribe una frase en la pizarra?**
  → **No, el profesor no escribe una frase en la pizarra. El profesor escribe una frase en el papel.**

1. vivir en una casa moderna (el estudiante)

   _____

   _____

2. recibir un regalo muy bonito (el padre)

_____

_____

3. correr en el parque (el perro)

_____

_____

4. abrir la puerta (el monstruo)

_____

_____

5. dividir la pizza (Pablo)

_____

_____

6. comer una banana (el mono)

_____

_____

7. describir la ópera (la mujer)

_____

_____

8. salir de la casa los domingos (los niños)

_____

_____

EJERCICIO A

Describe each picture using a form of **estar**.

1. El turista *está* en Nueva York.

2. José Antonio _____.

3. ¿Dónde _____ la universidad?

4. Tú _____.

5. La ventana _____.

6. Nosotras _____.

7. El café _____.

8. El cine _____.

9. Los amigos _____.

10. Los alumnos _____.

EJERCICIO B

Describe each picture using a form of **ser**.

1. Yo _____.   **2.** Los abuelos _____.

3. El muchacho _____.   **4.** La mujer _____.

5. Mi padre _____.   **6.** ¿ _____ Uds. _____?

7. Mis hermanos _____.

8. Sultán _____.

9. Somos _____.

10. La mamá de Graciela _____.

EJERCICIO C

Complete each sentence with **ser** or **estar**, as needed.

1. María _____ triste hoy.

2. Mi tía _____ abogada.

3. Yo _____ mexicana.

4. Ella _____ tocando la guitarra.

5. El agua _____ muy fría.

6. ¿Cómo _____ Uds. hoy?

7. ¿_____ ellos profesores?

8. ¿Dónde _____ tus libros?

9. ¿_____ gordo el gato de Javier?

10. Nosotros _____ enfermos.

EJERCICIO D

Finish the sentences below by changing the form of the verb **estar** and writing the opposite of the adjective.

EXAMPLE: Ella está muy triste hoy, pero Uds. **están muy contentos.**

1. Después de correr en el parque, ellos están sucios, pero Josefa _____.

2. La mochila está cerrada, pero la gaveta _____.

3. Yo estoy bien, pero mis hermanos _____.

4. Las hijas están contentas, pero la mamá _____.

5. El café está caliente, pero la limonada está _____.

6. Tú y yo estamos alegres, pero la profesora _____.

7. Ella está enferma, pero nosotros _____.

8. Las ventanas están abiertas, pero la puerta _____.

EJERCICIO E

Rewrite the following sentences substituting the words in parentheses for the subjects and making all necessary changes.

FOR EXAMPLE: Los muchachos no están contentos hoy. (el muchacho)
              El muchacho no está contento hoy.

1. Ella está enferma. (nosotros)

   _____

2. Yo no estoy bien. (Felipe)

   _____

3. Los gatos están limpios. (el perro)

   _____

4. Federico está contento. (mis padres)

_____

5. Ustedes están tristes. (Juan y Manolo)

_____

6. Mi amigo está cansado. (yo)

_____

7. La leche está fría. (el café)

_____

8. Los perros están en el parque. (Julia y Damián)

_____

9. Ellos están en Brasil. (mi abuelo)

_____

10. La sopa está caliente. (las hamburguesas)

_____

EJERCICIO F

Complete with the proper form of **estar**.

1. El médico _____ en el hospital.

2. Yo _____ bien, gracias.

3. ¿Dónde _____ mis hijos?

4. María _____ hablando por teléfono.

5. Nosotros _____ enfermos hoy.

6. Rosa y Felipe _____ en casa.

7. Las casas _____ en Nueva York.

8. ¿Dónde _____ tú ahora?

9. La comida _____ fría.

10. Los alumnos _____ sentados.

EJERCICIO G

Underline the form of **ser** or **estar** that correctly completes the sentence.

1. Yo (soy, estoy) enfermo.

2. Los edificios (son, están) nuevos.

3. Nosotros (somos, estamos) mexicanos.

4. Mi casa (es, está) grande.

5. El señor Molina (es, está) joven.

6. Mis abuelos (son, están) muy viejos.

7. Pablo y María (son, están) cantando.

8. El café (es, está) frío.

9. Tú y yo (somos, estamos) en la playa.

10. ¿Por qué (eres, estás) triste?

EJERCICIO H

Using a form of **ser** or **estar**, write sentences with the words provided.

EXAMPLE: mis hermanos/aquí
Mis hermanos están aquí.

1. La escuela/abierta

   _____

2. Felipe/abogado

   _____

3. Rosa/mexicana

_____

4. Antonio y José/cansados

_____

5. tú/de Quito

_____

6. tú/en Quito

_____

7. los muchachos/estudiar

_____

8. la comida/buena

_____

9. yo/norteamericano

_____

10. nosotros/amigos

_____

EJERCICIO A

Tell what the next day is.

1. Hoy es martes. Mañana es _____.

2. Hoy es viernes. Mañana es _____.

3. Hoy es lunes. Mañana es _____.

4. Hoy es miércoles. Mañana es _____.

5. Hoy es domingo. Mañana es _____.

6. Hoy es jueves. Mañana es _____.

7. Hoy es sábado. Mañana es _____.

EJERCICIO B

Fill in the blanks with the missing months.

1. enero   5. mayo   9. _____

2. _____   6. _____   10. _____

3. _____   7. julio   11. _____

4. _____   8. _____   12. diciembre

EJERCICIO C

Name the month suggested by the pictures.

1. _____

2. _____

3. _____

4. _____

5. _____

6. _____

7. _____   8. _____

9. _____   10. _____

EJERCICIO D

¿Antes o después? Give the day that comes before and after the day indicated.

1. lunes: antes del _____

2. sábado: después del _____

3. viernes: antes del _____

4. jueves: después del _____

5. miércoles: antes del _____

6. martes: después del _____

7. domingo: antes del _____

EJERCICIO E

Write out the circled dates in Spanish.

EXAMPLE: **Hoy es domingo, 6 de octubre.**

	ENERO	FEBRERO	MARZO	ABRIL
LUNES	7 14 21 28	4 11 18 25	4 11 18 25	1 8 15 22 29
MARTES	1 8 15 22 29	5 12 19 26	5 12 19 26	2 9 16 23 30
MIÉRCOLES	2 9 16 23 30	6 13 20 (27)	6 13 20 27	3 10 17 24
JUEVES	3 10 17 24 (31)	7 14 21 28	7 14 21 28	4 11 18 25
VIERNES	4 11 18 25	1 8 15 22	1 (8) 15 22 29	5 12 19 26
SÁBADO	5 12 19 26	2 9 16 23	2 9 16 23 30	6 13 20 27
DOMINGO	6 13 20 27	3 10 17 24	3 10 17 24 31	(7) 14 21 28

	MAYO	JUNIO	JULIO	AGOSTO
LUNES	6 13 20 27	3 (10) 17 24	1 8 15 22 29	5 12 19 26
MARTES	7 14 21 28	4 11 18 25	2 9 (16) 23 30	6 13 20 27
MIÉRCOLES	1 8 15 22 29	5 12 19 26	3 10 17 24 31	7 14 21 28
JUEVES	2 9 16 23 30	6 13 20 27	4 11 18 25	1 8 15 22 29
VIERNES	3 10 17 (24) 31	7 14 21 28	5 12 19 26	2 9 16 23 30
SÁBADO	4 11 18 25	1 8 15 22 29	6 13 20 27	(3) 10 17 24 31
DOMINGO	5 12 19 26	2 9 16 23 30	7 14 21 28	4 11 18 25

	SEPTIEMBRE	OCTUBRE	NOVIEMBRE	DICIEMBRE
LUNES	2 9 16 23 30	7 14 21 28	4 (11) 18 25	2 9 16 23 30
MARTES	3 10 (17) 24	1 8 15 22 29	5 12 19 26	3 10 17 24 31
MIÉRCOLES	4 11 18 25	2 9 16 23 30	6 13 20 27	4 11 18 (25)
JUEVES	5 12 19 26	3 10 17 24 31	7 14 21 28	5 12 19 26
VIERNES	6 13 20 27	4 11 18 25	1 8 15 22 29	6 13 20 27
SÁBADO	7 14 21 28	5 12 19 26	2 9 16 23 30	7 14 21 28
DOMINGO	1 8 15 22 29	(6) 13 20 27	3 10 17 24	1 8 15 22 29

1. _____

2. _____

3. _____

4. _____

5. _____

6. _____

7. _____

8. _____

9. _____

10. _____

11. _____

12. _____

EJERCICIO F

Complete these Spanish sentences.

1. Un año tiene _____ meses.

2. _____ es el primer mes del año.

3. _____ es el último mes del año.

4. El mes de junio tiene _____ días.

5. Si hoy es lunes, mañana es _____.

6. Si hoy es el primero de enero, mañana es _____.

7. No vamos a la escuela los sábados ni los _____.

8. Hay vacaciones largas en _____ y _____.

9. El Día de la Independencia es el 4 de _____.

10. El Día de Año Nuevo es el primero de _____.

EJERCICIO G

You have not been feeling well and have been unable to attend school. Some of your classmates have texted you and some sent you get-well e-mails. Answer each of your friends by thanking them for their concern and telling them how you feel. Don't forget to answer each of their questions in your reply.

Querido amigo:

¿Cómo estás? Estás muy enfermo? ¿Qué pasa?

¡Suerte! ¡ADIÓS!

_____

_____

_____

_____

_____

_____

_____

_____

Archivo Editar Ver Insertar Formato Opciones Herramientas Ayuda

Enviar | Ortografía | Adjuntar | Seguridad | Guardar

De:

Para:

Asunto:

Cuerpo del texto   Anchura variable

Querido amigo:

Estamos muy preocupados. ¿Cómo estás? ¿Estás aburrido en la casa? ¿Estás triste? Por favor, envía un mensaje pronto.

Con cariño,
Tus amigos de la clase de español.